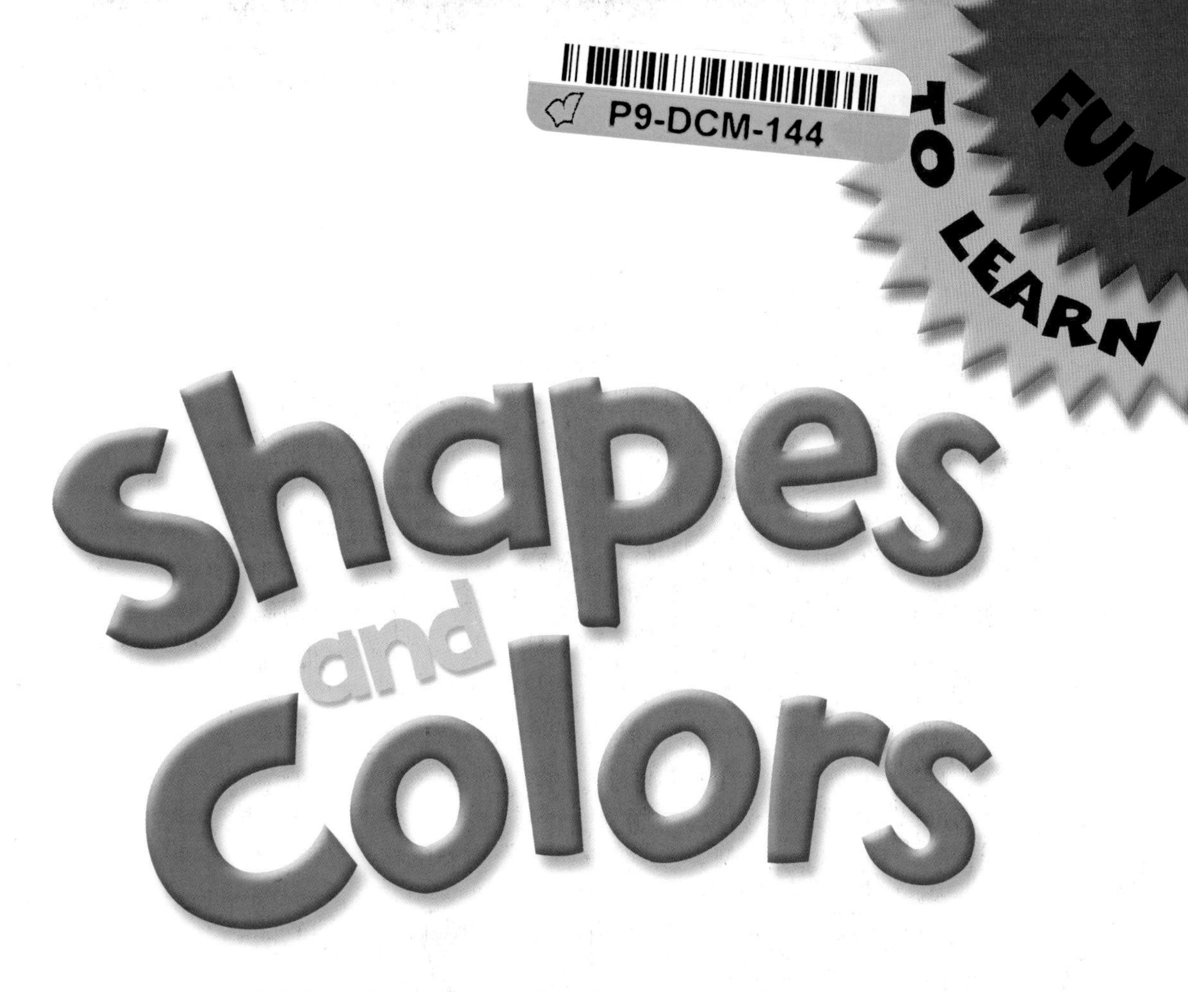

Shapes and Colors

Words by Nina Filipeck
Illustrated by Jan Smith

book-studio

Tim Smith
26 Main Street
Anytown
USA 11100

Tim gets a card.

What shape is the card?

What color is the envelope?

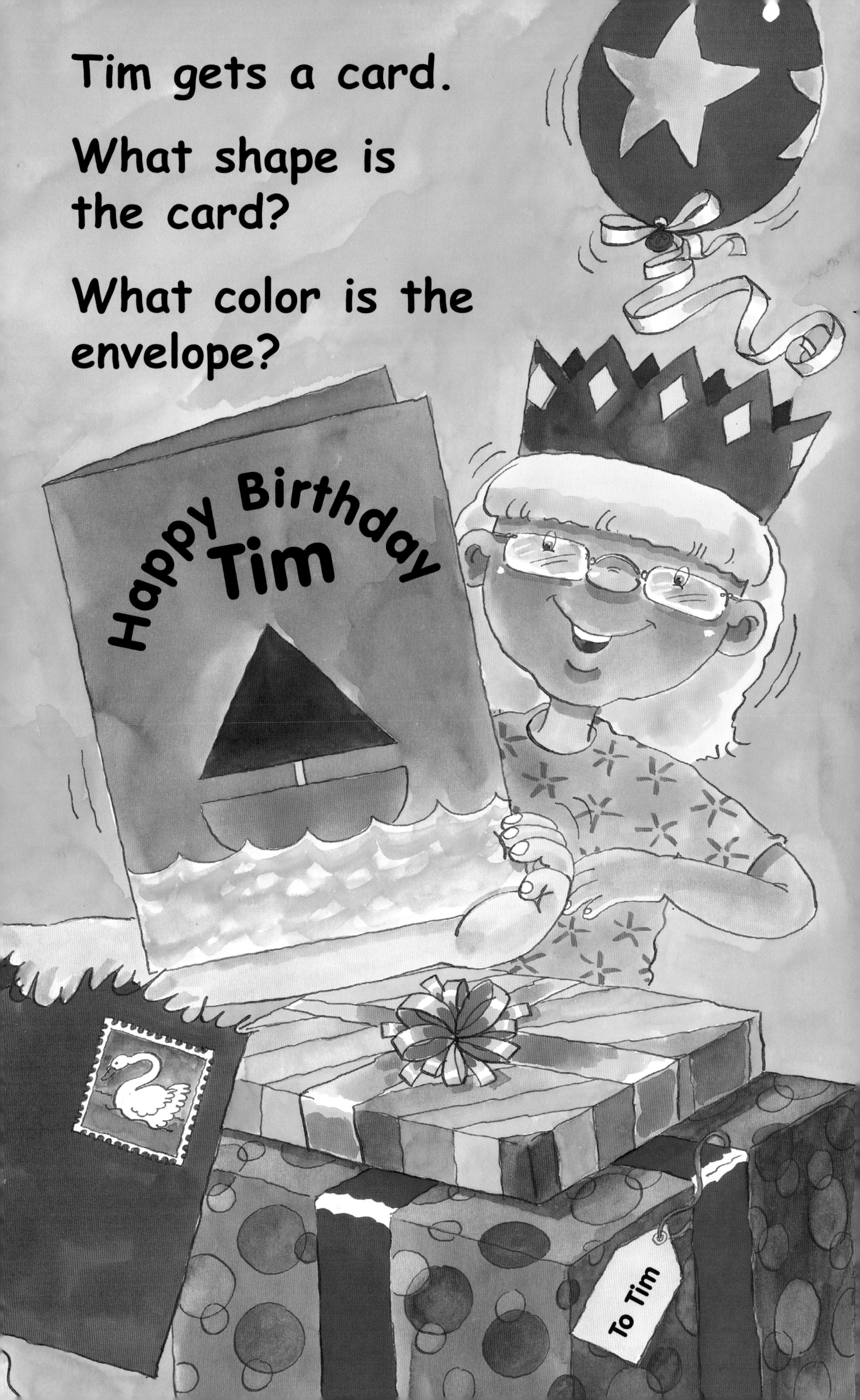

Tim gets a book.

What shape is the book?

What color is Tim's T-shirt?

Tim's Notebook

Happy
Birthday
Tim

Dad gives Tim a big box.

Tim wonders what's inside.

What shape is the box?

What color is the ribbon?

It's a sailboat!

Tim carefully lifts it from the box.

What shape is the sail on the boat?

What color is the boat?

Mom gives out
the drinks and
lollipops.

What shape are
the lollipops?

What color are the drinks?

Dad joins in the party games.

Tim gives Dad a party hat
and a balloon.

What shape is the party hat?

What color is the balloon?

Everyone has a party favor bag and a piece of chocolate cake.

What shape can you see on the bag?

What color is the cake?

Tim makes a “thank you” card for Mom and Dad.

What shape is on the card?

What color is the table?

Tim enjoyed
his birthday.

Now he's fast
asleep.

What shapes and
colors can you
see in his room?

The end